Beyond the Romantic Spirit

1880–1922

Book 1

Selected, edited and annotated by Nancy Bachus

19 Early Intermediate to Late Intermediate Piano Solos Reflecting
Society, Style and Musical Trends at the Turn of the 20th Century

Cover art: *Interior with Piano*
by Fernand Lantoine (1876–1936)
Waterhouse and Dodd, London, Great Britain
Fine Art Photographic Library, London/Art Resource, New York

Alfred

Contents

The author wishes to thank Ross Alley for his perceptive insights into this time period and Fernando Laires, Marcia Wellman and Kim Bakkum for their continued help and support.

Foreword

To understand and interpret musical style, one must recapture the spirit of the environment in which composers lived, created and performed, and be aware of influential events of the time. As composers approached the 20th century, the concept of one path, or a common musical language, predominant in art music for the preceding 300 years, ceased to exist. Increased communication and transportation brought a more global awareness. Western musicians were introduced to art and music from many countries and cultures. For the first time, several styles of art music existed simultaneously as composers consciously tried to write original music.

Reactions to 19th-Century Romanticism

At the **turn of the 20th century, there were numerous musical styles,** and music was in a state of flux. The emotional openness of late 19th-century Romantic music was embarrassing to many composers. They felt the need for greater restraint from this outpouring of uncontrolled passion and rejected that tradition. Other composers continued writing in the Romantic style but expanded some of the techniques. Several composers wrote in different styles at different times of their lives. Composers at this time were using all the resources of the past and creating anew. What they held in common was that they were all **reacting to 19th-century Romanticism** with their individuality and creating new styles.

Selected Music Styles at the Turn of the 20th Century

- **Post-Romantic**—The Romantic tradition continued with some individual changes.

- **Impressionism**—Associated most with the music of Claude Debussy, its vague and atmospheric tone paintings frequently violated traditional rules of composition.

- **Pointillism**—Written in a fragmented style, the ear is required to blend the tones.

- **Exoticism and Primitivism**—Inspired by primitive cultures and works of art, rhythm was revitalized and superseded melody in importance.

- **Neo-Classicism**—More contrapuntal textures and 18th-century forms reappeared (suites, toccatas, sonatas) using 19th-century harmonies.

- **Humor and Satire**—Some composers satirized the pretentiousness of Romantic music and poked fun at everything, including themselves.

- **Expressionism**—Intensely personal feelings were expressed with focus on dark, even weird and twisted emotions that are usually hidden from others.

- **Atonality**—Increased chromaticism and dissonance make tonal centers unclear to the listener, or the use of a tonal center or key is rejected by a composer.

- **Nationalism and Folk Influence**—Research into folk elements of various regions and countries gave greater harmonic and rhythmic variety to the musical language.

- **Cakewalk and Ragtime**—The music for the cakewalk became associated with ragtime with its "ragged," uneven, syncopated melodies over a march-like bass.

It is sometimes difficult to accept music that is different and has unfamiliar sounds, but it has always been that way. In 1600 the Italian composer Giovani Maria Artusi (1540–1613) stated, *"They...ruin the good old rules handed down...by theorists and excellent musicians... These moderns...create a tumult of sounds, a confusion of absurdities."*[1]

[1] Joseph Machlis, *Introduction to Contemporary Music* (New York: W. W. Norton & Co., 1961), 1.

Into the 20th Century

Political Changes

- In the late-19th century, many European countries showed renewed **interest and pride in their national traditions.** One manifestation of this was the establishment of Italy as a unified nation state in 1861 followed by Germany in 1871.

- Many countries **expanded their empires** by establishing colonies in parts of China, Africa and the South Pacific. In addition to the economic benefits, this also introduced new cultural elements to each country.

- Famine and social unrest in Russia at the turn of the 20th century culminated in the **Bolshevik Revolution** of 1917. This revolution and **World War I** (1914–18) caused many artists and intellectuals to leave their native countries. Many chose Paris, France, or cities in the United States for their permanent homes.

Scientific Advancements

Advances in transportation and communication changed everyday life for all classes of people.

- Thomas Alva Edison (1847–1931) invented the **phonograph** in 1877.

- Guglielmo Marconi (1874–1937) sent a trans-Atlantic **wireless radio** message in 1901.

- **Taxicabs** arrived in London in 1904, and production of the **Model T automobile** began in Detroit in 1907.

- Wilbur Wright (1867–1912) and Orville Wright (1871–1948) had a successful **flight** in 1903.

- **International expositions** held in London, Paris and Philadelphia in the late-19th century displayed commercial products, new technology and developments in the arts.

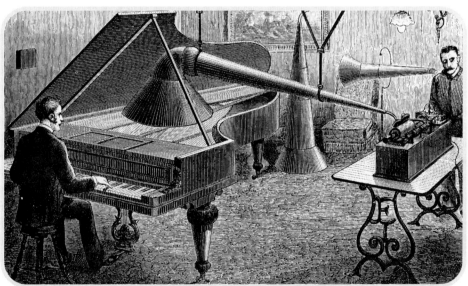

Recording a piano on an Edison phonograph (Paris, 1899)

© Image Select/Art Resource, NY

Social Trends

Cities were growing, and education (both general and in music schools) became more widespread, increasing the demand for all types of music. Symphony orchestras were founded, and music moved from salons to public concert halls, supported mainly by paying audiences.

"The pull-away from Romanticism was the most important interest of the early-20th century."

Aaron Copland (1900–1990), American composer[2]

ost-Romanticism in Music

Post-Romantic composers continued in the Romantic tradition with personal changes. Critics said they were out of step with progress and living in the past. One composer associated with the post-Romantic style was **Jean Sibelius** (1865–1957).

Jean Sibelius

Sibelius wrote in all forms except opera. His fame began with his symphonic poem, *Finlandia* (1900), which roused feelings of patriotism as his homeland suffered under the regime of the Russian Czar, Nicholas II (1868–1918). Sibelius became known as "Finland's greatest son."

Well known in his lifetime for his seven symphonies, he was a living legend throughout the world. In an interview for *Etude* magazine in 1948, he stated his philosophy: *"Things are not good because they are old, nor bad because they are new...we must be open-minded about new experiments in music, always remembering the only standard in music is beauty."[3]*

---

[2] Ibid., 6.

[3] Leroy V. Brant, "Sibelius Today," *Etude Magazine* (December 1948): 726.

Jean Sibelius wrote over 100 piano solos, mostly short salon pieces with programmatic titles. *Valsette*, written in 1912, is from a set of 10 miniatures entitled *Pensées lyriques* (Lyric Thoughts).

Valsette from *Pensées lyriques*

Jean Sibelius (1865–1957)
Op. 40, No. 1

ⓐ The editor suggests using "waltz-style" pedaling in this piece, lifting the damper pedal on beat 3.
A pedal pattern of **down-hold-up** works well for most of this waltz.

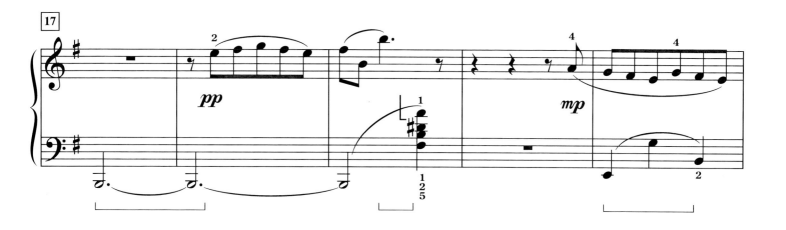

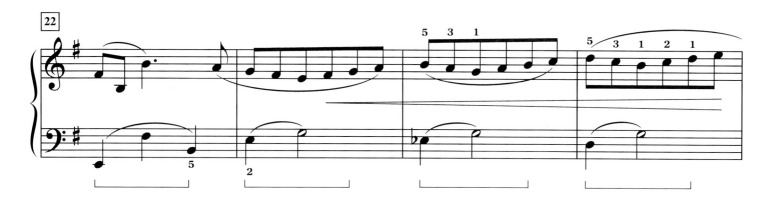

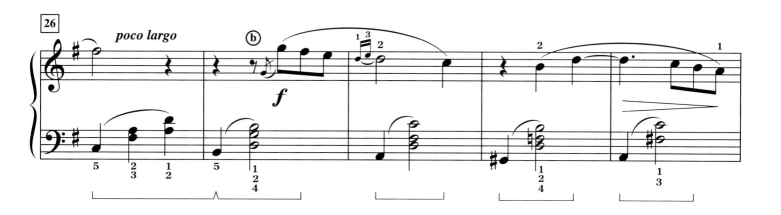

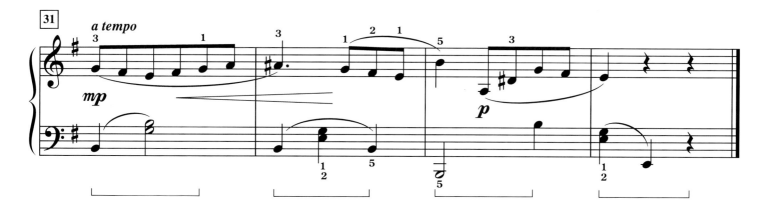

ⓑ The editor suggests that grace notes be played before the beat.

"Impressionism is at the root of all modern art, because it was the first movement that managed to free itself from preconceived ideas, and because it changed not only the way life was depicted but the way life was seen."

Francesco Salvi, writer[4]

*I*mpressionism

Impressionism, originating in France, was a movement in **art and music** in the late-19th and early-20th centuries.

Impressionism in Art

When an art critic saw **Claude Monet's** (1840–1926) painting entitled *Impression, soleil levant* (Impression, Sunrise), he described the entire exhibition (which included works by other artists) as one of "Impressionists," implying the works were sloppy and unfinished. These disparaging comments became a label for a style in the arts.

Impression, soleil levant *(1872)*
by Claude Monet

© Planet Art

Discarding the heroic themes of the Romantics, Impressionist artists **painted everyday life and people:** ballerinas, picnics, café scenes and nature. A fleeting impression, personal "snapshot" or emotional reaction to a scene was caught, not detailed.

- Before the Impressionist art movement, artists tried to portray exactly what the eye saw. With the development of photography in the 19th century, cameras could do this perfectly, freeing artists to go in new directions.

- Although some Impressionistic art lacked sharp outlines, the artists used a scientific approach. Fascinated by how sunlight breaks color into separate elements, many painted outdoors using tiny brush strokes of pure color on the canvas. The blending of the colors was left to the eye of the observer.

- Artists studied light reflections on water, clouds, mist, haze, smoke, and gardens, and Monet studied the reflection of light on objects at different times of the day. He painted the Cathedral in Rouen, France, 20 times under different light conditions.

[4] <www.impressionism.org>

Impressionism in Music

Away from Tonality and Chromaticism

The **major/minor tonal system** was used in Western music approximately from the Renaissance to 1900. It is based upon **seven-note scales** with a gravitational pull to a **home note** or **tonic**, a concept called **tonality**. Tension is resolved when that tonic pitch is reached. However, there are 12 half-steps in an octave. When the **other five pitches** are used for expressive coloring or to suggest another key, it is called **chromaticism**.

In the late-19th century, many composers felt this **system of tonality was exhausted**; nothing new could be said in this framework. New techniques were developed that violated traditional rules of harmony and obscured tonality (yet did not destroy it). Adopted by many composers, these techniques are associated with **Impressionistic musical style**.

"A century of aeroplanes deserves its own music. As there are no precedents, I must create anew."
Claude Debussy[5]

The Influence of Debussy

In 1887, **Claude Debussy** (1862–1918) was warned to *"avoid vague impressionism [in his music], since this is one of the most dangerous enemies of truth in art."*[6] Debussy disliked the term, but the blurred harmonies, and atmospheric moods he created have linked him with the movement.

Claude Debussy

- Impressionism is sometimes called the "twilight of Romanticism" because it frequently depicts nature, has programmatic titles, and emphasizes beautiful sound—all Romantic characteristics.

- Influenced by the Impressionistic painters, Debussy created tonal paintings of nature in *La mer* (The Sea), *Reflets dans l'eau* (Reflections on the Water), *Le vent dans la plaine* (The Wind over the Plain) and *Brouillards* (Fog). He even used **art terms** such as *Images*, *Estampes* (engravings) and *Esquisses* (sketches) as titles.

- Debussy disliked the excess of the four-hour-long music dramas by the German composer **Richard Wagner** (1813–1883). Debussy reacted by creating music that was understated, transparent in texture, and rooted in his French heritage.

- Debussy urged French composers to rediscover the clarity and elegance of the Baroque harpsichord composers, **François Couperin** (1668–1733) and **Jean-Philippe Rameau** (1683–1764), and create music of elegance and charm that would please and entertain. He proudly signed his name, *"Claude Debussy, musician of France."*

---

[5] Ian Crofton & Donald Fraser, *A Dictionary of Musical Quotations* (New York: Schirmer Books, 1985), 47.

[6] *New Grove Dictionary of Music and Musicians*, s.v. "Impressionism" (London: Macmillan, 1980), 30.

"To study music, we must learn the rules. To create music, we must break them."

Nadia Boulanger (1887–1979),
20th-century composition teacher[7]

Techniques of Impressionistic Music

- **Pedal (or organ) point**—A chord or tone is sustained by the damper pedal, while other chords move above it. This gives a "hazy" background with a melody "painted" over it.

- **Unresolved chords in parallel motion**—Chords were seen as **independent, vertical sonorities** (a color). These chords (either blocked or broken) were shifted up or down. Rather than resolving traditionally, they **glide** in **blocks of unresolved harmonies.**

- **Nonmetrical rhythm**—With this technique, the music lacks a regularly occurring (measured) accent. Sound flows continuously from measure to measure, avoiding the *tyranny of the bar line* or an accent on every beat one.

- **Other techniques** used are **irregular phrase lengths** and **melodies** that are often **fragmentary motives** (repeated). Debussy frequently employed **unusual scale patterns** (not major or minor), such as **pentatonic** (five notes) or those based on **medieval church modes.**

Reinhold Glière (1875–1956) was one of many Russian composers to be influenced by Debussy's music.

- His career transitioned the "old" Russian regime to the "new" Soviet government. He won a gold medal in composition from the Moscow Conservatory and gained international fame with his Symphony No. 3, Op. 42. The ballet *Krasnïy mak* (The Red Poppy) is his most famous work.

- He taught at the Kiev Conservatory, served as its Director, and joined the Moscow Conservatory faculty in 1920, remaining there until his death. **Sergei Prokofiev** (1891–1953), **Nikolai Miaskovsky** (1881–1950), and **Aram Khachaturian** (1903–1978) were among his students.

Reinhold Glière

---

[7] Joseph Machlis and Kristine Forney, *The Enjoyment of Music* (New York: W. W. Norton & Co., 1999), 503.

Reinhold Glière's *Le soir* (The Evening) is Impressionistic in style. Composed in 1909, its vague, mysterious mood depicts the title. The undulating **rhythmic ostinato** (repeated pattern of F-sharps) in the left hand helps paint the picture.

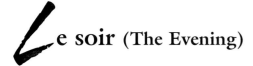

Le soir (The Evening)

Reinhold Glière (1875–1956)
Op. 43, No. 5

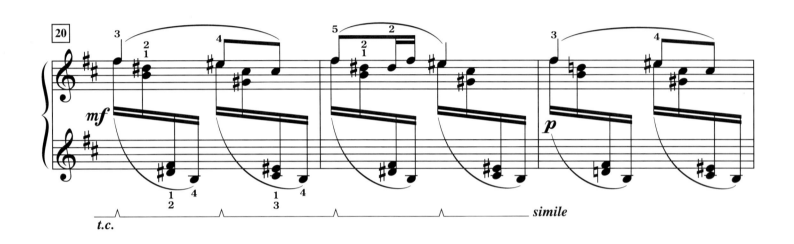

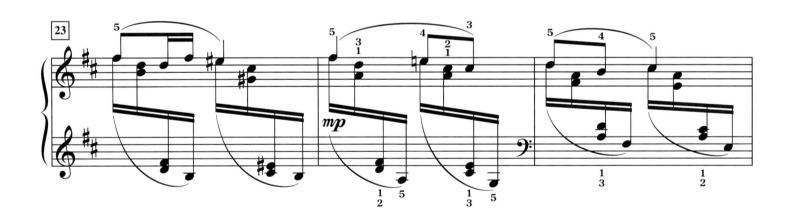

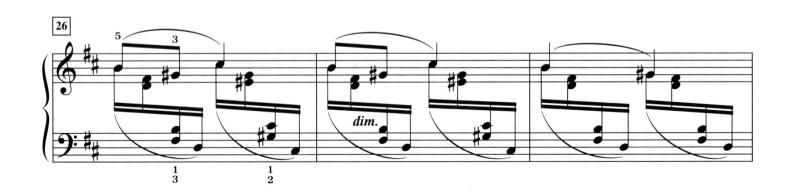

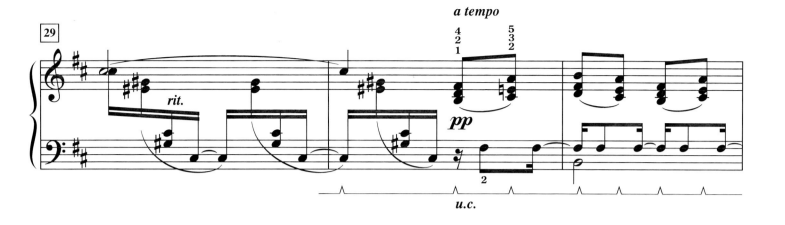

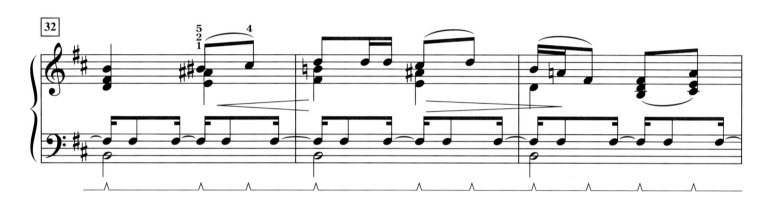

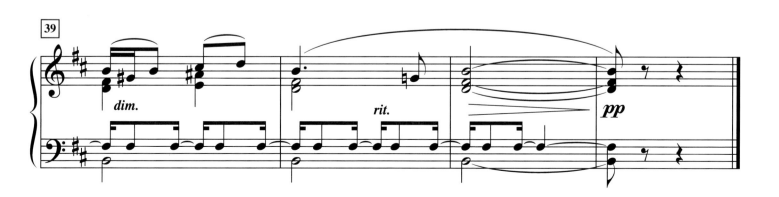

This waltz-like piano solo of **Claude Debussy** was written in 1915 and left untitled. It is thought to have been composed for a benefit auction that provided clothing for soldiers wounded in World War I.

Album Leaf

Claude Debussy
(1862–1918)

ⓐ Debussy's metronome marking.

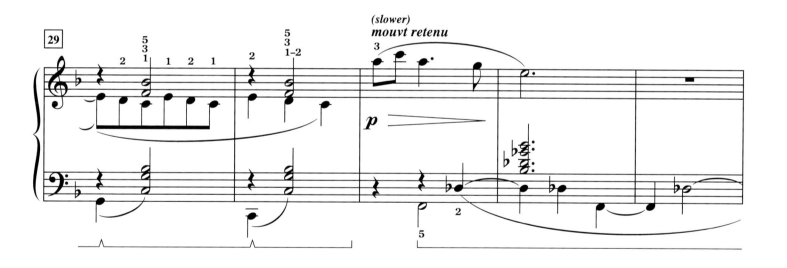

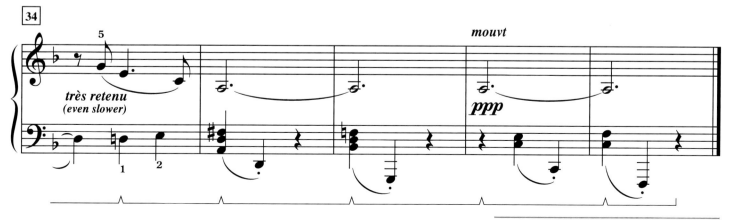

Maurice Ravel used some Impressionist techniques, but his music has more Classical traits than Debussy. His phrases are more clearly defined, frequently balanced in two- to four-measure units set off by cadences. This *Prélude* was written as a sight-reading examination for students at the Paris Conservatory.

 rélude

(Rather slow and very expressive [with free rhythm])
Assez lent et très expressif (d'un rythme libre)

Maurice Ravel
(1875–1937)

ⓐ The pedal indication ⎺⌇⌇⌇⌇⌇⎺ in measures 9, 17 and 19 means to flutter or shake the damper pedal to thin out the texture.

[8] Charles Stanley, notes to *Maurice Ravel, the Complete Piano Music* (Vox Productions, Inc., n.d.).

ⓑ Fade out the entire sound by fluttering or shaking the damper pedal.

Pointillism (Neo-Impressionism)

Pointillism in Art

Impressionist painters studied the rapid changes of light and color on objects, painting as they experienced it with rapid brush strokes. Carrying this technique to extreme, some artists used **thousands of little dots** or **points of color**, a style known as **pointillism** or **neo-impressionism**.

- **Georges Seurat** (1859–1891) was the founder of the French school of **pointillism.** In his short life, he painted a few very large works, spending a year or more on each. He wanted to restore order, calmness, and monumentality to painting while using new Impressionistic techniques.

- Seurat was the ultimate scientist and spent his life studying color theories and the effects of different line structures. Each of the multitude of colored dots becomes a "building block" in the total structure. When looking at the paintings from a distance, the individual dots cannot be seen, only the larger solid shapes and objects.

- Small areas have vibrancy and subtle variations of color as images that do not exist appear almost miraculously before the eye. His paintings have an **abstract** feel.

A Sunday Afternoon on the Grande Jatte (1884–86) by Georges Seurat

© Planet Art

Pointillism in Music

Another reaction to Romanticism in music was to avoid continuous musical lines and textures and write in a more **fragmentary style**, often using extreme contrasts in range. This is sometimes referred to as **pointillism in music** because the **ear** is required to **make connections between the musical tones** as the eye connected dots in pointillistic paintings. Carl Nielsen's *Jumping Jack* (page 22) uses the pointillistic technique of **octave displacement**.

---

[9] Laurence Madeline, *100 Impressionist Masterpieces, Musée d'Orsay* (Paris: Éditions Scala, 1999), 15.

Toward Abstraction

Away from Reality

The scientific study of color by Impressionist and pointillist artists helped them realize the **expressive power of color and shapes.** Some artists began to express themselves through just colors and/or forms, moving away from reality toward the **abstract art** of the 20th century.

Cubism in Art

Pablo Picasso (1881–1973) frequently depicted his subjects three-dimensionally with geometric shapes. He is the founder of a style of painting known as **cubism.**

Picasso, and other cubists, observed that views are different while walking around an object. They painted all the views from different perspectives simultaneously, making some parts clearly focused and others more blurred.

Woman with Mandolin *(1909)*
by Pablo Picasso

© Erich Lessing/Art Resource, NY

New Harmonic and Rhythmic Techniques

Musicians at this time also experimented with new ways of expressing themselves and developed new techniques that made music appear more abstract.

- **Tonality** implies that **one key** or tonal center is dominant. Some composers began using **two keys simultaneously**, called **bitonality.**

- Others used **more than two keys** simultaneously, called **polytonality.**

- **Chords** moving outside a tonal framework, called **polychordal** music, is another approach.

- Some composers stopped dividing music into measures, **omitting bar lines and time signatures** in the score, to give rhythm a more natural, speech-like flow.

[10] Derek Watson, ed., intro. and selection, *Dictionary of Musical Quotations* (Ware Hertfordshire: Cumberland House, Wordsworth Editions Ltd., 1994), 84.

Vladimir Rebikov was born in Russia and studied at the Moscow Conservatory and in Berlin, Germany. His teaching pieces for piano represent many different compositional styles, including **post-Romantic, Impressionistic,** and more **abstract** or **contemporary** pieces such as *The Vast Expanse of Space*. This work has **no bar lines or time signature** to divide the music into measures and is **polychordal**. The right hand is firmly in C major while the left hand plays different chords (major, minor, and an augmented chord) against it. Some theorists call this **displaced harmony**.

The Vast Expanse of Space

Vladimir Rebikov
(1866–1920)

ⓐ Since there are no bar lines or key signature, all notes should be played in relationship to a steady quarter-note beat.

Carl Nielsen is considered by many to be the greatest Danish composer of all time. He wrote in many different musical styles and forms during his lifetime, and is best known for his symphonies. *Jumping Jack,* from his six *Humorous Bagatelles,* is **abstract** in style.

The piece opens with a C minor triad, followed by an F-sharp diminished triad. The **pointillistic technique of octave displacements** (where chord tones are separated by a wide keyboard range) confuses the ear since the tones are heard separately, not as chords. Ending this phrase on a D major chord is not typically done in traditional, functional harmony. Because all these **patterns are repeated**, the ear soon adjusts.

Jumping Jack from *Humorous Bagatelles*

Carl Nielsen (1865–1931)
Op. 11, No. 4

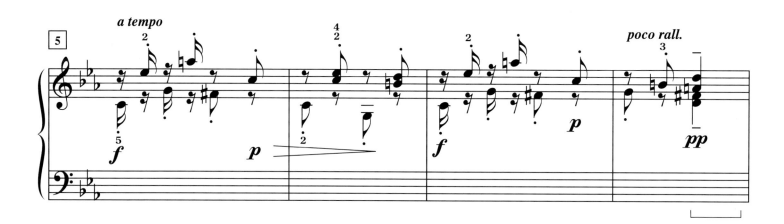

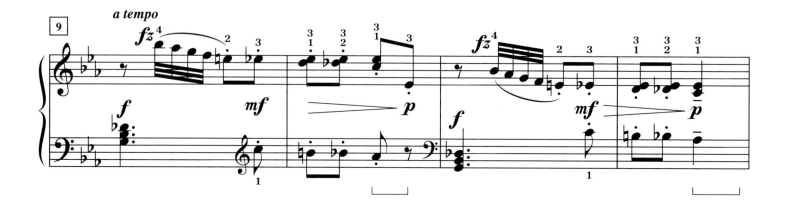

Exoticism and Primitivism

During the 18th and 19th centuries, **all non-Western music** was described as **exotic.** Arabian, Persian and Asian elements found their way into the West as artists and musicians evoked the mystery of these far-off lands.

Intrigued by "exotic" cultures, artists began to idealize "primitive" societies for their simple, natural life unaffected by education and the responsibilities of modern society. A reaction against science, technology and civilization, **primitivism** was another movement away from Romanticism at the turn of the 20th century.

African mask from the Ivory Coast

Masks of this type appeared in Paris in the early 1900s and impacted artists. These masks were worn as part of tribal rituals and celebrations that included prayer, song and/or dance.

Neo-Primitivism in Art

Non-Western art influenced modern artists. An exhibit of folk arts from Africa, Australia and Oceania was held in Paris in the late-19th century. European art was transformed as artists used the bold colors, original designs and expressiveness of these "primitives" in a style known as neo-primitivism.

The artist **Paul Gauguin** (1848–1903) turned to primitive cultures for inspiration and moved to Tahiti for two years. After his return to Paris, he became dissatisfied and left his "civilized," middle-class life permanently, spending the rest of his life in the South Sea islands. Gauguin used vivid colors and flat forms, rather than three-dimensional perspective, in his art.

Two Tahitian Women and a Dog (1893) by Paul Gauguin

© Scala/Art Resource, NY

---

[11] William Fleming, *Arts and Ideas* (Philadelphia: Holt, Rhinehart & Winston Inc., 1991), 481.

"Rhythm and motion, not the element of feeling,
are the foundations of musical art."
Igor Stravinsky, 20th-century composer[12]

Primitivism in Music

Pulsating rhythms and harsh dissonances that assault the ear bring to life scenes and images of primitive cultures to create **primitivism in music.** Melody became less important as rhythm and motion became more prominent.

- **Béla Bartók's** (1881–1945) *Allegro barbaro* (1911), with its motoric, "barbaric" rhythms exploits the **percussive aspects of the piano** more than its lyrical qualities.

- The ballet score from *The Rite of Spring* (1913) of **Igor Stravinsky** (1882–1971) creates images of pagan rites through irregular rhythms, **ostinatos** (repeated accompaniment figures) and an orchestration of eerie, brutal, even savage sounds that deliberately renounce traditional ideas of beauty.

Costumes of the Russian tribal maidens, from Stravinsky's The Rite of Spring

Whole-Tone Scale

This scale **divides the octave into six equal parts,** with no half-step divisions. The lack of half-steps gives a sense of vagueness and indecision since there is no pull for resolution to any note. The right-hand melody in Vladimir Rebikov's *The Bear* (page 26) is based on a whole-tone scale.

The Whole-Tone Scales

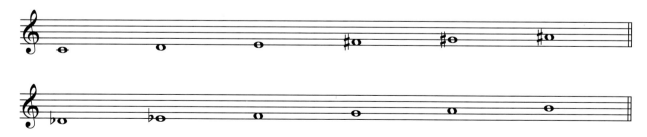

[12] Machlis, *Introduction to Contemporary Music*, 40.

The Bear suggests **primitivism** with the unrelenting left-hand **rhythmic ostinato**.

he Bear

Vladimir Rebikov
(1866–1920)

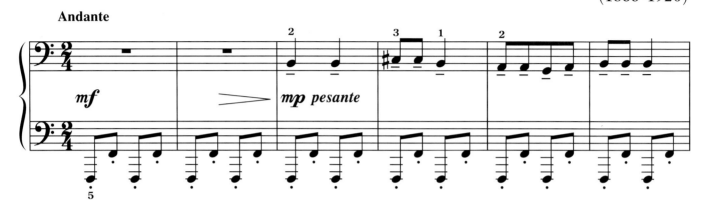

*N*eo-Classicism

Some composers reacted to Romantic music by **turning away** from tone paintings with **programmatic** stories and pictorial associations. They preferred **absolute music**, which has no extra-musical inspiration and gives greater emphasis to form and structure.

Seventeenth- and eighteenth-century **compositional techniques and forms** were revived and used in a nineteenth-century harmonic framework. Contrapuntal textures were more frequent as toccatas, fugues, suites, inventions, variations, and sonatas reappeared.

German-born, **Max Reger's** (1873–1916) training emphasized his German heritage. He created organ studies by adding a third part to **Johann Sebastian Bach**'s (1685–1750) *Two-Part Inventions* and has been nicknamed "the second Bach."

Max Reger

Courtesy of the
Max Reger Institute

- Highly respected as a pianist, conductor and teacher, his fame is greatest in Germany. He has been the subject of more than 25 books, but very few have been translated.

- Reger wrote chamber music, choral and orchestral works, and songs. He has been called the *"most important organ composer since J. S. Bach"*[14] and also wrote over 150 works for piano.

[13] David Ewen, *The World of 20th Century Music* (Englewood Cliffs, NJ: Prentice-Hall, 1980), 642.
[14] *New Grove Dictionary*, s.v. "Max Reger."

Gigue (page 28), the ninth piece in **Max Reger's** *Ten Little Performance Pieces*, is in the typical Baroque binary form. Gigues were usually in $\frac{6}{8}$ time and were used as the last movement of Baroque dance suites. Reger added a subtitle to this set, "for teaching purposes."

Gigue from *Ten Little Performance Pieces*

Max Reger (1873–1916)
Op. 44, No. 9

"An artist must organize his life. Here is the exact timetable of my daily activities. Get up: 7:18 AM; be inspired: 10:23 to 11:47 AM. I take lunch at 12:11 PM and leave the table at 12:14 PM."

Erik Satie[15]

Humor and Satire

French composer, **Erik Satie** (1866–1925) reacted to the excesses of Romanticism by writing in a simple, bare bones style with wit and mockery. Music critic and composer, **Virgil Thomson** (1896–1989) considered Satie the *"most original mind in modern music."*[16]

Always a rebel, Erik Satie dropped out of the Paris Conservatory after a year and began writing humorous piano music. He published his first pieces as Op. 64, and the 180-note *Vexations* had instructions to repeat it 840 times. Instructions on another piano piece were, *"To be played with both hands in the pocket."* Supposedly when Debussy told him his music lacked form, he responded with *Three Pieces in the Shape of a Pear.*

"See no evil, Hear no evil, Speak no evil." Left to right: Marcel Duchamp (1887–1968), artist; Erik Satie, musician; and James Joyce (1882–1941), author

- Satie earned his living as a cabaret pianist and song writer for popular entertainers in the Montmartre region of Paris. His best-known piano pieces, *Gymnopédies* (1888), with their sparse texture and haunting melodies, were orchestrated by Debussy.

- Around age 40, he began formal studies in music composition and earned a diploma. In his satirical ballet, *Parade* (1917), in collaboration with artist, **Pablo Picasso** and writer, **Jean Cocteau** (1889–1963), the score used American ragtime style, a typewriter, fire sirens, and airplane motors as well as traditional musical instruments.

- He used modal harmonies, changing meters, and was one of the first to write rhythmic notation without bar lines. Satie anticipated the **Dadaist movement** where artists deliberately used incomprehensible methods to shock, for the purpose of questioning accepted values in the arts.

Bathing in the Sea (page 31) is from a set entitled *Sports and Divertissements* (Recreations) and consists of 20 one-page pieces. They all include commentary to the performer and are written without bar lines. Some of the other titles are *Fishing, Golf,* and *Fireworks.*

[15] Crofton & Fraser, 131.

[16] Norman Lebrecht, *The Companion to 20th Century Music* (New York: Simon & Schuster, 1992), 301.

Bathing in the Sea from *Sports and Divertissements*

Erik Satie
(1866–1925)

La mer est large, Madame.
(The ocean is wide, Madame.)

En tout cas, elle est assez profonde.
(In any case, it is rather deep.)

Ne vous asseyez pas dans le fond. C'est très humid.
(Do not sit on the bottom. It is very wet.)

Voici de bonnes vieilles vagues.
(Here come some good old waves.)

Elles sont pleines d'eau.
(They are full of water.)

Vous êtes toute mouillée!
(You're all wet!)

Oui, Monsieur.
(Yes, sir.)

(With motion and emotion)
ⓐ Mouvementé

11 avril 1914
(April 11, 1914)

ⓐ Since there are no bar lines, all notes should be played in relationship to a steady quarter-note beat.

Expressionism

Expressionism is a term used to describe a trend in European art, literature, theater and music at the turn of the 20th century. Influenced by **Sigmund Freud's** (1856–1939) psychological studies of the subconscious mind, artists focused on the **expression of inner feelings and responses to a scene** rather than a realistic depiction. They used distortion and exaggeration to create emotional intensity. Their emphasis on the strange, macabre, abnormal, even warped and twisted, has been seen by some as the **final agonizing stage of Romanticism.**

The Scream (*1893*)
by Edvard Munch

Expressionism in Art

Expressionistic painters, with their emotional approach to art, discarded traditional ideas of beauty and contorted the external world. They delved into mental states unseen by the eye through vivid colors, exaggerated perspective, and extreme contrasts of light and shade.

Edvard Munch (1863–1944), a Norwegian painter who studied in Paris and Berlin, was a major influence on other expressionist artists. He used heavy brushstrokes and distorted faces and figures in his neurotic paintings that studied human terror. Perhaps this helped him cope with the tragedies of his own life, which included the premature deaths of his mother and sister. In *The Scream*, the viewer can see fear.

Expressionism in Music

The musical leader of the expressionist movement was **Arnold Schoenberg** (1874–1951). Like expressionistic artists, expressionistic composers discarded what had been accepted as beautiful. They developed new techniques to create maximum emotional intensity.

- They used violent texts in operas and deliberately distorted normal speech patterns when setting words, and favored melodies with angular shapes and wide leaps.

- Instruments were used in extreme ranges, and the traditional concept of **tonality** with dissonance and resolution **was eventually discarded**.

[17] Machlis, *Introduction to Contemporary Music*, 335.

tonality

To express a wider range of emotions, late-Romantic composers used increased **chromaticism** and dissonance to make tonal centers less clear-cut. When **tonality is unclear** to the listener, or the use of a **tonal center** or **key is rejected** by a composer, this is known as **atonality** (without tonality). Another reaction to Romanticism was the discarding or **disintegration of tonality**, forcing composers to find new ways to organize their music.

Charles Griffes in Central Park (1918)

A native of Elmira, NY, **Charles Griffes**'s (1884–1920) first piano teacher paid for him to study in Berlin. Planning to become a concert pianist, he had successful performances, but during his four years abroad, he became more interested in composition.

After his father died, he returned to the United States and accepted a teaching position at the Hackley School in Tarrytown, NY. He held this position, and helped support his mother, brothers, and sisters until his untimely death at age 35.

- His early works, especially his art songs, show German influence, and many of the piano pieces reflect **Impressionistic** elements. However, his *Piano Sonata* (1918) reflects a complete break from his earlier style in a powerful and dissonant work with no programmatic elements. Pianist, Rudolf Ganz (1877–1972) called it *"the finest abstract work in American piano literature."[19]*

- The year before his death (1919), Griffes was working on some short piano pieces. First published in 1967 as *Three Preludes*, they are his last completed works for piano.

- Compared to Arnold Schoenberg's **expressionistic** *Six Little Piano Pieces*, Griffes's *Three Preludes* **verge on atonality**. The expressive *Prelude No. 2* is organized around a repeated, haunting motive and appears **atonal** until the final cadence gives a feeling of F minor.

"We can no longer tolerate this fetishism of tonality, which has been a burden on entire generations of musicians."
Arthur Honegger (1892–1955), composer[20]

[18] Watson, 4.

[19] Edward Maisel, *Charles T. Griffes, the Life of an American Composer* (New York: Alfred A. Knopf, 1984), 272.

[20] David Pickering, *Cassell Companion to 20th Century Music* (London: Cassell, 1998), 23.

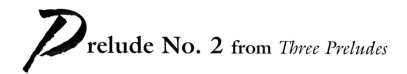

Prelude No. 2 from *Three Preludes*

Charles Griffes
(1884–1920)

Lento misterioso

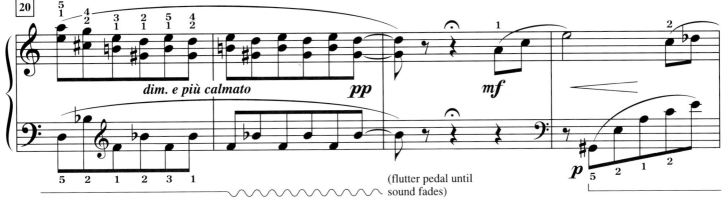

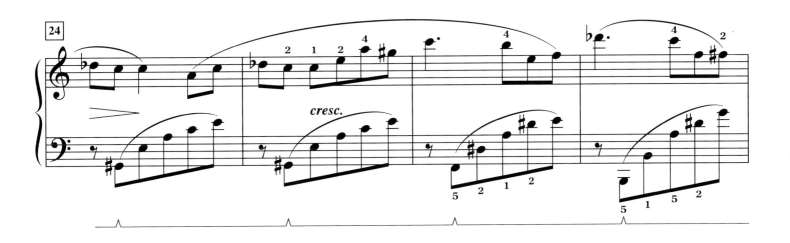

"Every composer cannot expect to have a worldwide message, but he may reasonably expect to have a special message for his own people."

Ralph Vaughn Williams (1872–1958), English composer[21]

Nationalism and Folk Influence

As European nations struggled for freedom and independence in the 19th century, many composers **intentionally used national elements** (folk melodies, dance rhythms, and themes that reflected their country's history or culture) in their works.

Somewhat a reaction to the dominance of German and Italian music, **nationalism** was strong in Russia in the 19th century, and in Bohemia (Czech Republic), Scandinavia, Spain, Hungary, the United States and Latin America at the turn of the 20th century.

"Authentic" Folk Music and Musicology

The earliest nationalist composers, attracted to the spontaneous and unsophisticated qualities of folk music, incorporated them in their concert works, paying little attention to the origins of the material. As this continued, composers began to **research their country's musical heritage** in both the art and folk traditions.

The Spaniard **Felipe Pedrell** (1841–1922) believed national character in music could best be developed by integrating the masterpieces of a country's art music with authentic folk music. One of the first **musicologists**, he **researched Spanish music**, collecting and compiling many volumes of folk songs as well as art music from previous centuries.

Courtesy of the Bartók Archives, Budapest

Bartók recording a folk song in a Hungarian village

[21] Machlis, *Introduction to Contemporary Music*, 256.

Hungary

Bartók transcribing music he had collected

While in Transylvania, **Béla Bartók** (1881–1945) heard a young woman sing an unusual song she had learned from her mother, and this began his lifelong fascination with the **folk music of Hungary**. For many years, Bartók traveled to remote areas of Hungary, Eastern Europe and the Middle East, frequently accompanied by **Zoltan Kodály** (1882–1967), the Hungarian composer, ethnomusicologist and educator. Bartók recorded peasant performances on an Edison phonograph and then transcribed, analyzed and catalogued the thousands of collected peasant melodies.

Courtesy of the Bartók Archives, Budapest

To most of the 19th-century musical world, Hungarian music meant the *Hungarian Rhapsodies* of **Franz Liszt** (1811–1886) and the *Hungarian Dances* of **Johannes Brahms** (1833–1897). Folk songs are present in these works, but the material was derived from music of the itinerant **gypsies of Hungary**. This is a small part of the true Hungarian folk music discovered, organized and published by Bartók and Kodály.

Born in Hungary, Bartók showed exceptional talent as a child, composing piano pieces at nine and performing the Sonata No. 21 ("Waldstein"), Op. 53, of **Ludwig van Beethoven** (1770–1827) at ten. Known as a virtuoso, Bartók was appointed to the piano faculty at the Budapest Academy of Music in 1907, only four years after his graduation. His piano works range from a beginning method to exceedingly difficult concertos.

- Bartók's immersion into folk music greatly influenced his compositions. He did not simply quote folk themes; they became a part of him, and he expressed himself through the unusual rhythms, melodies and scales that became his unique language.

- Bartók taught only piano, not composition, during his nearly 30 years at the Academy. From all accounts, he was a patient teacher who insisted on all details, yet his emphasis was more musical than technical.

- *For Children* is a two-volume set that includes **85 folk song transcriptions for piano**. They bring together Bartók's interests in folk music and in piano teaching. He stated in 1940 that he had written these pieces because he felt there was a shortage of materials for beginning pianists with "real musical value."[23]

- Bartók wrote a variety of articulation markings in his music that must be observed.

---

[22] Crofton & Fraser, 66.

[23] David Yoemans, *Bartók for Piano* (Bloomington: Indiana University Press, 1988), 35.

Translated lyrics of this Hungarian folk song:

The sun shines into the church, whoopee! The priest tolls the bell for the first time, whoopee!
The priest enters to preach, whoopee! To marry the little brunette girl, whoopee!
She can hardly wait to be wed, whoopee! To leave the altar, whoopee!

This piece has **changing meters.** Keep the quarter note beat steady throughout the piece.

Hungarian Song No. 32 from *For Children*, Part 1

Béla Bartók
(1881–1945)

Translated lyrics of this Hungarian folk song:

My little graceful girl is dressed in white,
My darling is dressed in white; I say, turn to me, my married bride.

Round Dance No. 17 from *For Children*, Part 1

Béla Bartók
(1881–1945)

Spain

Many factors contributed to the richness of **Spanish folk music**. The **various regions** have distinct **cultural differences** with some having their own language, due in part to geographical conditions. The many mountain ranges create natural barriers and great variations in climate. Proximity to France and North Africa, plus invasions in different parts of the peninsula introduced Jewish, Christian, Muslim, Gypsy and other traditions. Spanish colonists also brought elements back from the Americas.

Born in the region of Catalonia, **Isaac Albéniz** (1860–1909) was such a prodigy on the piano, that he was compared to **Wolfgang Amadeus Mozart** (1756–1791). His piano works suggest images of his native land as he ushered in *"Spain's golden age of piano music."*[24]

- Performing in Barcelona at age four, his mother took him to Paris when he was six. Too young to enroll in the Paris Conservatory, he studied privately with a professor. He published his first composition in Spain and enrolled at the Madrid Conservatory at age eight.

- There are many stories that suggest he frequently ran away from home to concertize. Said to have been a stowaway on a ship to Argentina at age 12, he did perform in Cuba and Puerto Rico at a young age. He studied briefly in Leipzig and won first prize in piano at the Brussels Conservatory at 19.

- About this time, Albéniz came under the influence of the Spanish musicologist, **Felipe Pedrell**, and began to incorporate Spanish folk elements in his compositions.

Isaac Albéniz

[24] Linton E. Powell, *A History of Spanish Piano Music* (Bloomington: Indiana University Press, 1980), 49.

Capricho catalan is from the *España* suite. Typical of songs from Catalonia, it is in a major key with unusual chromaticism in the melody.

Capricho catalan from *España*

Isaac Albéniz (1860–1909)
Op. 165, No. 5

ⓐ The editor suggests that grace notes be played before the beat.

Also born in the Spanish region of Catalonia, **Enrique Granados** (1867–1916) was a few years younger than Isaac Albéniz. They are often linked together since both were outstanding pianists, studied in Paris and were students of the Spanish musicologist, Felipe Pedrell.

Enrique Granados

- Inspired by art of **Francisco Goya** (1746–1828), a set of pieces called *Goyescas* is Granados's best-known work for piano. Due to its popularity, he was commissioned to base a full-scale opera on it. In 1916, Granados attended the world premiere of the opera, *Goyescas*, at the Metropolitan Opera in New York City. On his return voyage, a German submarine torpedoed the ship, and he and his wife drowned in the English Channel.

- Deeply rooted in Romanticism and preferring miniature forms, Granados's piano style has been described as Chopin-esque with Spanish overtones. *Vals sentimental* and *Vals brillante* (page 48), from a set of short, poetic waltzes, are in this style.

Vals sentimental No. 6 from *Valses poético*

Enrique Granados
(1867–1916)

ⓐ The editor suggests that grace notes be played before the beat.

ⓑ Optional ending: A low F-sharp played on beat 1 of
the final measure can make a more conclusive ending.

Vals brillante No. 5 from *Valses poético*

Enrique Granados
(1867–1916)

Allegretto (elegante)

Cuba

Cuban music is a multitude of styles and types. European style art music was present in Cuban cathedrals as early as the mid-16th century, but influences from Africa and Spain dominated.

- The *contradanza* became the most popular 19th-century **Cuban ballroom dance** and evolved into a **miniature form for solo piano**, never intended for dancing. It is believed French refugees from Haiti imported the *contredanse* to Cuba. Black musicians then dotted and syncopated the rhythms, gave it a slower tempo (due to the climate) and created the *contradanza* or **habanera** (from Havana), which influenced the tango.

Habanera rhythms:

(**Habanera:** Afro-Cuban dance and song and/or Havana-style *contredanse*)

A virtuoso pianist and composer, **Ignacio Cervantes** (1847–1905) was the first Cuban composer to achieve international fame.

- Born in Havana to a professional family, he had fine musical training. When the American composer-pianist **Louis Moreau Gottschalk** (1829–1869) visited Havana, he was so impressed by the seven-year-old Cervantes that he took him as a pupil and later arranged for him to study at the Paris Conservatory.

- In Paris, Cervantes won first place in the piano competition as well as prizes in harmony, fugue and counterpoint. As a foreigner, he was not eligible for the top compositional *Prix de Rome*. An anecdote tells that while practicing in Paris, Cervantes was interrupted by **Franz Liszt** who was so impressed by the playing, he stopped to meet the performer and then asked permission to stay and listen.

- Cervantes wrote in many forms including symphony and opera, but his best-known works are his piano pieces. In 1870, he returned to Havana, teaching, conducting and concertizing until his death.

Ignacio Cervantes in his Havana studio

Ignacio Cervantes integrated native Cuban elements with European Romantic piano style to create **Cuban concert or art music**. *Los tres golpes* (The Three Strikes) is one of his 45 *Danzas cubanas* (Cuban dances) that have sold thousands of copies since their publication between 1875 and 1885. These popular dances have two 16-measure sections (sometimes repeated) with varied endings, and feature syncopated, dance-like patterns similar to the cakewalk and tango.

Los tres golpes Danza cubana

Ignacio Cervantes
(1847–1905)

ⓐ The editor suggests that grace notes be played before the beat.

> *"The way to write American music is simple. All you have to do is to be an American and then write any kind of music you wish."*
>
> Virgil Thomson, American composer and critic[25]

America

American music is difficult to define because, like America itself, it has great diversity. Sprouting from European culture, it has grown into something unique.

- The first great native-born composer was probably **Stephen Foster** (1826–1864), whose songs have become so well known, many consider them to be American folk songs.

- **Edward MacDowell** (1860–1908), with European study, performances and publications, had an international reputation when he returned to the United States in 1887. His piano miniatures, such as *To a Wild Rose,* reflect his American heritage.

- In 1885, a patroness of the arts, **Mrs. Jeannette Thurber** (1850–1946) founded a National Conservatory in New York with a charter from the United States Congress and an international faculty. In 1892, the Czech composer, **Antonin Dvořák** (1841–1904), became the Director of the school and composed his famous *Symphony from the New World* (Op. 95) at this time. He urged American composers to use **native American folk music (Indian and Negro melodies)** in their music to create a unique American style.

Amy Beach

One composer active in the Boston area at the turn of the 20th century was **Amy Cheney Beach** (1867–1944), a virtuoso pianist who performed with the Boston Symphony at age 17. After her marriage, she limited her public performances and focused more on composition. She responded to Dvořák's advice with her *Gaelic Symphony* by using **folk themes from Ireland and Scotland**, the music of her European ancestors. This was the first symphony by an American woman ever performed anywhere in the world, and it was played dozens of times by orchestras in the United States and Europe during her lifetime.

Cover from 1907 edition of Eskimos

[25] Machlis, *Introduction to Contemporary Music,* 327.

Considered by many to be the founder of American anthropology, **Franz Boas** (1858–1942) lived with Eskimos and published *The Central Eskimo* in 1888. Included in the data he collected and published were **Inuit** or **Eskimo** folk songs. In 1907, Beach composed a set of piano pieces titled *Eskimos* that used these themes. The second piece in the set, *The Returning Hunter* is based on an Inuit song that was sung by the women as they watched for a hunter's return, according to Boas.

The Returning Hunter *from the 1888 publication of* The Central Eskimo *by Franz Boas.*[26]

The Returning Hunter from *Eskimos*

Amy Cheney Beach (1867–1944)
Op. 64, No. 2

[26] Franz Boas, *The Central Eskimo* (Sixth Annual report, Bureau of Ethnology, The Smithsonian Institution, 1888), 653.

The American composer, **Robert Nathaniel Dett** (1882–1943), is credited with raising the Negro spiritual to the level of art song. He edited collections of spirituals and folk songs and used them in choral works and piano pieces. His compositions were widely known during his lifetime.

Robert Nathaniel Dett

- Dett held music degrees from several prestigious institutions including the Oberlin Conservatory, Harvard University and the Eastman School of Music. He also studied composition in France with **Nadia Boulanger**.

- At Oberlin, a performance of a Dvořák string quartet reminded him of spirituals his grandmother had sung to him as a child. This was the beginning of his lifetime efforts to integrate folk and art music.

Paul Laurence Dunbar (1872–1906), the son of former slaves, was the first African-American to gain fame as a poet. He also wrote in other forms and was popular in his lifetime with both black and white readers. He had two styles: standard English and the dialect of black Americans, and has been compared to **Mark Twain** (1835–1910) for his ability to convey character through dialect.

A Negro Love Song
by Paul Laurence Dunbar

Seen my lady home las' night,
Jump back, honey, jump back.
Hel' huh han' an' sque'z it tight,
Jump back, honey, jump back.
Hyeahd huh sigh a little sigh,
Seen a light gleam f'om huh eye,
An' a smile go flittin' by—
Jump back, honey, jump back.

Hyeahd de win' blow thoo de pine,
Jump back, honey, jump back.
Mockin'-bird was singin' fine,
Jump back, honey, jump back.
An' my hea't was beatin' so,
When I reached my lady's do',
Dat I could n't ba' to go—
Jump back, honey, jump back.

Put my ahm aroun' huh wais',
Jump back, honey, jump back.
Raised huh lips an' took a tase,
Jump back, honey, jump back.
Love me, honey, love me true?
Love me well ez I love you?
An' she answe'd, "'Cose I do"—
Jump back, honey, jump back.

---

[27] Crofton & Fraser, 3.

Dett's best-known piano work is *In the Bottoms*. He wrote the following program notes for this suite:

The five numbers give pictures of moods or scenes peculiar to Negro life in the river bottoms of the southern sections of North America. It is possible to musically portray this without the use of actual folk songs. The third piece in the suite, "Honey" is a colloquialism—the familiar term of endearment (South)…the intimation here is one of coquetry. It is after "A Negro Love Song" by Paul Laurence Dunbar. Flirt all you please with "Honey."

Honey (Humoresque) from *In the Bottoms*

Nathaniel Dett
(1882–1943)

ⓐ The metronome markings are the composer's; however, this piece is also effective played at a slightly slower tempo.
ⓑ The grace notes should be played before beat 1, anticipating the beat and giving a jazz-like effect.

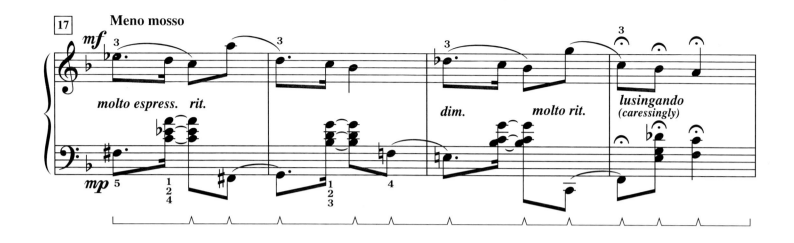

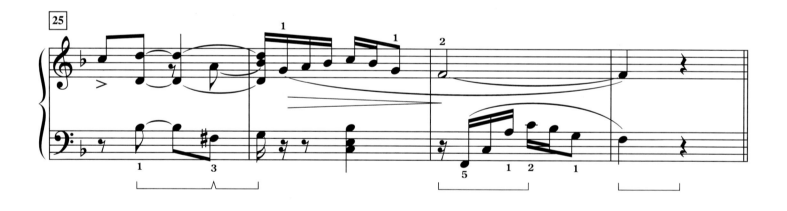

(A lot slower and in a speech-like style)

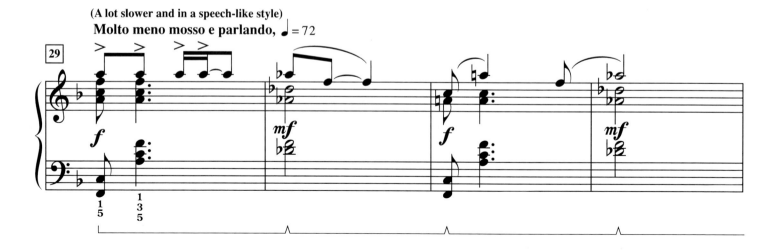

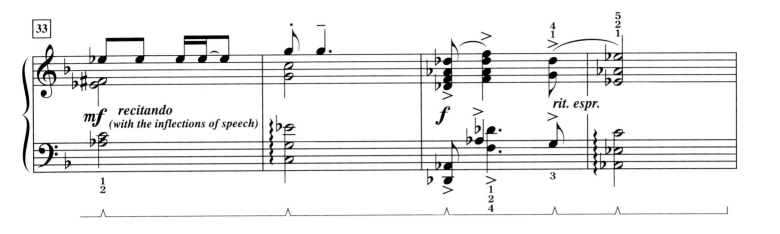

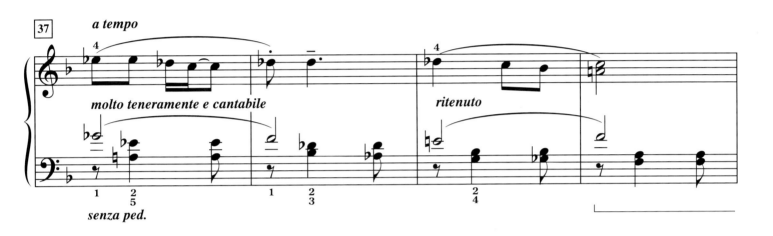

"...filthy and suggestive music has inundated the land...Nothing but ragtime prevails and the cakewalk with its obscene posturings, its lewd gestures."

The Musical Courier, 1899 (music magazine)[28]

Cakewalk and Ragtime

American Popular Music

Many trends, customs and musical genres merged late in the 19th century to create the American cakewalk and rag-time styles. (These terms were first used interchangeably.)

- **Cakewalks** were social events in small-town America. Well-dressed couples strolled and skipped to fiddler's tunes on a town square decorated by cakes on corner pedestals. When the music stopped, the couple nearest the cake took it home for Sunday dinner.

- Plantation owners sometimes held dancing contests for slaves where a popular prize was a cake. There were no specific steps for the **cakewalk dance**, but it was associated with exaggeratedly dignified couples strutting arm in arm with high kicks, bows, bending the body back, doffing hats and waving canes in a parody of their masters. The proclamation for the winning dance was, *"That takes the cake."*[29]

- The cakewalk appeared on the stage as a popular finale in minstrel shows, vaudeville and burlesque. In the 1890s it was introduced into ballrooms with champion "walkers" in New York City winning gold belts and diamond rings.

Cakewalking couple

The Cakewalk Goes International

The music for the cakewalk became associated with **ragtime** with its "ragged," uneven, syncopated melodies over a march-like bass. A completely American art form originated by black musicians in saloons, ragtime's popularity spread throughout the United States and Europe aided by the sales of millions of copies of printed sheet music.

Sheet music cover of a ragtime piece of Scott Joplin depicting the cakewalk dance

---

[28] Crofton & Fraser, 122.

[29] James Haskins, *Scott Joplin, The Man Who Made Ragtime* (New York: Scarborough House, 1980), 74.

The American band leader, **John Philip Sousa** (1854–1932), performed cakewalks with his band during his European tours. **Claude Debussy** attended one of these concerts in 1903 and also saw the cakewalk danced at American minstrel shows in Paris. Debussy captured the sophisticated humor of this popular American dance form in *Golliwogg's Cakewalk* (1908) and *Le petit nègre* (1909).

Le petit nègre

Claude Debussy
(1862–1918)

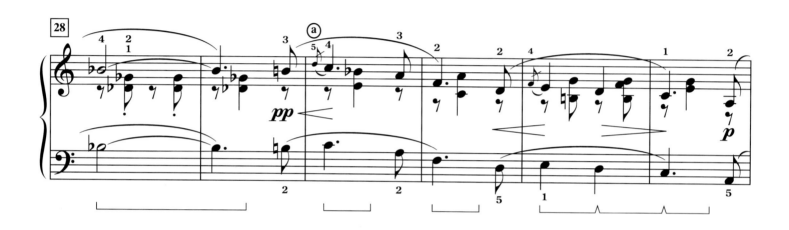

ⓐ The editor suggests that grace notes be played before the beat.

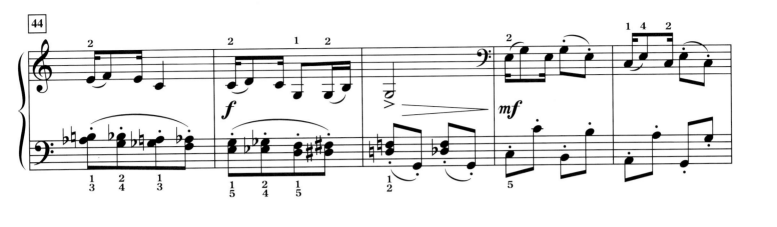